The Fourth Grade Election

by Chandler Roberts

Illustrated by Tom McKee

PEARSON

Scott
Foresman

Editorial Offices: Glenview, Illinois • Parsippany, New Jersey • New York, New York
Sales Offices: Needham, Massachusetts • Duluth, Georgia • Glenview, Illinois
Coppell, Texas • Sacramento, California • Mesa, Arizona

Dear Reader, on page 12 you will find a glossary with some of the words we use in this book to talk about elections.

teacher

It was a very important day in Mrs. Chang's fourth grade class. Today the children would have their first election for class president.

"Being class president is an important job," said Mrs. Chang. "The class president will do many things. Last year, our class president was Giselle López. Giselle asked the rest of the fourth graders to read stories for kindergarten children."

"What else did the president do?" asked Tanisha.

"Giselle and the other fourth graders planned a bake sale," answered the teacher. "Some of the children made cookies. Some children brought cakes. The fourth grade used the money to buy a fish tank for the science class. The president did a good job!"

The children heard about these things, and they were excited about the election. Many children wanted to be class president.

Mrs. Chang explained, "Being class president can be fun, but it is a big responsibility. Sometimes the president has to stay after school to make sure projects are done. The president has to be a good student. The president must be a good leader."

Karla raised her hand. "Mrs. Chang, how do we pick a class president?"

---

leader: person who leads or directs other people

"We will have an election. You students will vote," answered Mrs. Chang.

"It is very similar to how we select the leaders of our country. Let's start with the Constitution of the United States," Mrs. Chang said.

"The United States Constitution contains basic laws written by our country's first leaders. Those laws tell us how the United States must be governed.

"Our first leaders did not want a king. They wanted a president to lead the country. A president is someone whom the people choose. We Americans choose the president by voting."

Katrel asked, "Should we raise our hands to show we want a certain person to be class president?"

"We are not ready for voting yet," answered Mrs. Chang. "First, we have to pick the *candidates.* If many people think one person would be a good president, they nominate that person. They say, 'I think Student A would make a good president,' or 'I think Student B would make a good president.'

"If everyone agrees that these are people who would make a good president, they become the candidates. When we have the election, we choose one candidate. We pick Student A or Student B."

paper ballot

voting machine

"What if one candidate is my friend, but I want to pick a different candidate for president? If my friend knows I voted for someone else, she might not be my friend anymore," said Tanisha.

Mrs. Chang wrote something on the board: *secret ballot.* "In the United States, we have a secret ballot. When you vote for president, it is personal and private. No one may watch you vote. You go behind a curtain or into a little room. Then you choose the candidate you want. You are the only person who knows who it is. Your choice is a secret."

---

private: secret and personal

"Now," said Mrs. Chang. "It is time for us to begin our election. Who remembers what we have to do first?"

Karla raised her hand. "We have to nominate the candidates. First we have to think about students in the class who might make a good president. Then we say the name of a person we think would be the best."

"Does anyone have a person to nominate?" asked Mrs. Chang.

The children looked around the room. Some children looked at Katrel. He was very smart and always did his class work. He played baseball with the other children and always followed the rules. He was also on the Safety Patrol.

"I nominate Katrel," said Carlos. "He would make a good president." Four other children agreed. Mrs. Chang wrote Katrel's name on the board.

"Carlos nominated Katrel. Katrel is our first candidate," said Mrs. Chang. "Is there anyone else who would make a good president?"

The children looked around again. They looked at Tanisha. Tanisha was a class leader. She asked good questions in discussions. She paid attention in class. Every morning she walked her little sister to kindergarten. When she found Marta's dollar on the playground, she gave it back to Marta. Marta raised her hand.

"I think Tanisha would make a good candidate for president. I nominate Tanisha." Five other children agreed. Mrs. Chang wrote Tanisha's name on the board. The students were happy. They had nominated two good candidates.

"Now, children," said Mrs. Chang, "it is time to vote." She handed out little papers and pencils to the children. "Now you may write the name of one candidate on your paper. When you are finished, fold the paper so that no one can see it and put it in this box. This is a secret ballot. When you are finished, I will count the votes. And, remember, no matter who wins the election, our class will have a good president!"

ballot box

Glossary

bal•lot

(bal′ət), *NOUN*. **a piece of paper, card, or machine used in voting**

can•di•date

(kan′də dāt), *NOUN*. **a person who is suggested by others for an office or job**

e•lec•tion

(i lek′shən), *NOUN*. **a choice by voting. In an election, voters choose someone to fill an office such as president.**

nom•i•nate

(nom′ə nāt), *VERB*. **to name a candidate for an election**

se•cret bal•lot

(sē′krit bal′ət), *NOUN*. **a way of voting so that no one can see your ballot**

U•ni•ted States Con•sti•tu•tion

(yü nī′tid stāts kon′stə tü′shən), *NOUN*. **the basic laws that tell how the United States must be governed**

vote

(vōt), *VERB*. **to express a choice**